JAMES RAE

JAZZY DUETS
FOR SAXOPHONES
FOR YOUNG PLAYERS

www.**universal**edition.com

vienna · london · new york

UE 19 395

ISMN M-008-03899-0
UPC 8-03452-02066-0
ISBN 3-7024-2511-X

JAZZY SERIES

Young players of today are exposed to a variety of contemporary styles and this new series of jazzy and relaxing pieces for PIANO, FLUTE, CLARINET, SAXOPHONE, RECORDER and VIOLIN, attempts to provide players with experience of the syncopated patterns of Jazz, Rock and Pop music, whilst keeping within technical bounds which will have been achieved at various grades. Where appropriate, accompaniments have been kept deliberately simple to encourage other young players to act in this capacity.

Heutige junge Musiker sind einer Vielfalt zeitgenössischer Stile ausgesetzt. Diese neue Serie von jazzigen und entspannenden Stücken für KLAVIER, FLÖTE, KLARINETTE, SAXOPHON, BLOCKFLÖTE und VIOLINE, will versuchen, die Spieler mit der Praxis der synkopierten Muster in Jazz, Rock- und Popmusik vertraut zu machen, innerhalb der technischen Möglichkeiten, die schrittweise erreicht werden sollen.
Wo es zweckmäßig schien, wurden die Begleitstimmen absichtlich einfach gesetzt, um dadurch andere junge Musiker zum Mitspielen anzuregen.

This collection of five original pieces has been composed to give saxophonists of moderate ability the experience of playing duets in the jazz idiom. They can either be played by two saxophones in the same key (i.e. two altos, two tenors, alto and baritone, tenor and soprano, etc.) or by using the transposed second part, alto and tenor.

Grade: 4-5

Die vorliegende Sammlung besteht aus fünf Originalkompositionen, die geschrieben wurden, um Spielern mit begrenzten technischen Fertigkeiten die Möglichkeit zu geben, Duos im Jazzstil zu spielen. Die Stücke können entweder mit zwei Saxophonen in der gleichen Tonart (d.h. zwei Alt- oder zwei Tenorsaxophone, Alt- und Bariton- bzw. Tenor- und Sopransaxophon etc.) ausgeführt werden, oder, unter Verwendung der transponierten zweiten Stimme, mit Alt- und Tenorsaxophon.

Schwierigkeitsgrad: 3 (Skala 1-5)

CONTENTS

JAZZY DUETS

FOR SAXOPHONES

THE RIFFLE SHUFFLE

JAMES RAE

*May also be played in a driving rock tempo, i.e. even quavers: Kann auch mit Drive (d.h. mit gleichmäßigen Achteln) gespielt werden :

Universal Edition UE 19395

OFF THE RECORD

JAMES RAE

THE LATE, LATE BLUES

JAMES RAE

CONTRAFLOW

James Rae

Universal Edition

JAMES RAE

JAZZY DUETS

FOR SAXOPHONES

FOR YOUNG PLAYERS

TENOR SAXOPHONE

www.universaledition.com
vienna · london · new york

UE 19 395a

ISMN M-008-03899-0
UPC 8-03452-02066-0
ISBN 3-7024-2511-X

JAZZY DUETS

FOR SAXOPHONES

1

THE RIFFLE SHUFFLE

Tenor Saxophone

JAMES RAE

*May also be played in a driving rock tempo i.e. even quavers: Kann auch mit Drive (d.h. mit gleichmäßigen Achteln) gespielt werden:

Universal Edition UE 19395a

OFF THE RECORD

JAMES RAE

THE LATE, LATE BLUES

JAMES RAE

CONTRAFLOW

JAMES RAE

⑤

CHASE THE ACE

JAMES RAE

18826	P. HARVEY/J. SANDS	JAZZY CLARINET 1
19361	P. HARVEY	JAZZY CLARINET 2
18827	J. RAE	JAZZY SAXOPHONE 1
19362	J. RAE	JAZZY SAXOPHONE 2
19393	J. RAE	JAZZY TRUMPET 1
18825	J. REEMAN	JAZZY FLUTE 1
19360	J. REEMAN	JAZZY FLUTE 2
18824	J. REEMAN	JAZZY PIANO 1
19363	B. BONSOR/G. RUSSELL-SMITH	JAZZY PIANO 2
18828	G. RUSSELL-SMITH	JAZZY RECORDER 1
19364	B. BONSOR	JAZZY RECORDER 2
19431	M. RADANOVICS	JAZZY VIOLIN 1
19757	M. RADANOVICS	JAZZY VIOLIN 2
16553	M. RADANOVICS	JAZZY CELLO 1
19711	T. DRUMMOND	JAZZY GUITAR 1
19429	J. RAE	JAZZY DUETS FOR FLUTES
19430	J. RAE	JAZZY DUETS FOR CLARINETS
19395	J. RAE	JAZZY DUETS FOR SAXOPHONE
19396	J. RAE	JAZZY DUETS FOR FLUTE and CLARINET
19756	M. CORNICK	JAZZY DUETS FOR PIANO
16536	M. CORNICK	JAZZY DUETS FOR PIANO 2
16537	M. RADANOVICS	JAZZY DUETS FOR VIOLIN

CHRISTMAS JAZZ

19184	J. RAE	CHRISTMASJAZZ FOR FLUTE
19186	J. RAE	CHRISTMASJAZZ FOR TRUMPET
19187	J. RAE	CHRISTMASJAZZ FOR CLARINET
19188	J. RAE	CHRISTMASJAZZ FOR ALTO SAXOPHONE
19189	J. RAE	CHRISTMASJAZZ FOR CELLO
19190	J. RAE	CHRISTMASJAZZ FOR TROMBONE
19185	J. RAE	CHRISTMASJAZZ FOR VIOLIN

VI/94

UNIVERSAL EDITION

CHASE THE ACE

JAMES RAE

18826	P. HARVEY/J. SANDS	JAZZY CLARINET 1
19361	P. HARVEY	JAZZY CLARINET 2
18827	J. RAE	JAZZY SAXOPHONE 1
19362	J. RAE	JAZZY SAXOPHONE 2
19393	J. RAE	JAZZY TRUMPET 1
18825	J. REEMAN	JAZZY FLUTE 1
19360	J. REEMAN	JAZZY FLUTE 2
18824	J. REEMAN	JAZZY PIANO 1
19363	B. BONSOR/G. RUSSELL-SMITH	JAZZY PIANO 2
18828	G. RUSSELL-SMITH	JAZZY RECORDER 1
19364	B. BONSOR	JAZZY RECORDER 2
19431	M. RADANOVICS	JAZZY VIOLIN 1
19757	M. RADANOVICS	JAZZY VIOLIN 2
16553	M. RADANOVICS	JAZZY CELLO 1
19711	T. DRUMMOND	JAZZY GUITAR 1
19429	J. RAE	JAZZY DUETS FOR FLUTES
19430	J. RAE	JAZZY DUETS FOR CLARINETS
19395	J. RAE	JAZZY DUETS FOR SAXOPHONE
19396	J. RAE	JAZZY DUETS FOR FLUTE and CLARINET
19756	M. CORNICK	JAZZY DUETS FOR PIANO
16536	M. CORNICK	JAZZY DUETS FOR PIANO 2
16537	M. RADANOVICS	JAZZY DUETS FOR VIOLIN

CHRISTMAS JAZZ

19184	J. RAE	CHRISTMASJAZZ FOR FLUTE
19186	J. RAE	CHRISTMASJAZZ FOR TRUMPET
19187	J. RAE	CHRISTMASJAZZ FOR CLARINET
19188	J. RAE	CHRISTMASJAZZ FOR ALTO SAXOPHONE
19189	J. RAE	CHRISTMASJAZZ FOR CELLO
19190	J. RAE	CHRISTMASJAZZ FOR TROMBONE
19185	J. RAE	CHRISTMASJAZZ FOR VIOLIN

VI/94

UNIVERSAL EDITION